# Table of Contents

## Section I: Identifying oppression

## Section 2: Impact of oppression

## Section 3: Coping with oppression

## Section 4: Transforming our communities

## Epilogue:

# A Mutual Aid Publication by The Icarus Project

First edition, 2015.
Your input and ideas are welcome for future versions of this guide.

## Icarus Community Contributors:
NS, Teja Jonnalagadda, Melissa, Joshua#7, Jen, Brianne Nelson, Denise Auld, Lawrence S Grillo, Pretty Broken Riot, Isnnj, Ben, Moleman64, Cheyenna Weber, Daniela Capistrano, JSC, Sum Kitteh, Christa, Q, Deborah Machon, Lily Swann, L.P., Person, Jac, Paola Barba, Bryce Wagner, John, Amiyu, Jomal, Katherine, Maree, Daniel Spencer, Perla C., Elizabeth, JP, Sunlit Doorway, Renee Garcia, Alison, Emma, Real, Limeymama, KR, Dominic Bradley, KiWan, Fred Abbe, Amy H., Amalia, A.R.Corsi, Sam, Echo, Suki, Avery, Corvus, Sara, Kate, Cmplxwmn, J. Yoshida, Pam Arizona, ABBLE, Enzyme, David, Heather, Cathy, Missy, Danielle Patrick, Jessica Simpson, Adela Brent, Ms Y, Sarah Barbara, MConnolly, Lily, Billy De Voe, Greyjay, Petros Evdokas, Morganne, Deena, Imogen, Scrump, Natasha Joseph, Jackie, Gabrielle, Nabster, Corr, Jessica, Marianna, Regina Corsi, Littlewolf, Emily Waterpony, and dozens of people who wish to remain anonymous.

## Mad Maps Coordinator
Agustina Vidal

## Art and Design:
Cover Art: Mohammed Fayaz aka Mojuicy
Art Director: Steven Garcia

## Contributing artists:
JW Arndt, Eddy Falconer, Cara Hartley, Anastasia Keck, Till Krech, Jacks McNamara, Jess Rankine, Joey Wilbur, Jodi Bentivegna

## Editors:
Guide Editor-in-Chief: Agustina Vidal
Guide supporting editors: Cheyenna Layne Weber, Lauren Taylor Hudson, Daniela Capistrano

**Images courtesy of:** The Icarus Project Sacramento

This guide is available as a free file download at The Icarus Project website in online and printer-ready versions.

# What Are Mad Maps?

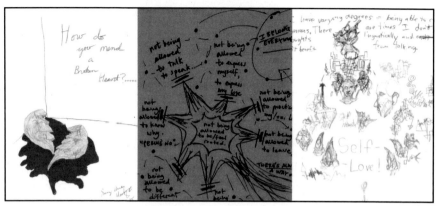

IMad Maps In Process image courtesy of Sacramento Icarus Project

In a world that seals up the side trails, hidden doors and underground caves, forcing us all to walk the arbitrary straight path of so-called normalcy, The Icarus Project is a respite for those who wish to explore the art of getting lost. Fueled by hope and creativity, our members have been artfully forging roads and making maps that define our journeys with mental health struggles in the context of a crookedly beautiful world. We have called these cartographic musings Mad Maps.

Mad Maps are documents that we create for ourselves as reminders of our goals, what is important to us, our personal signs of struggle, and our strategies for self-determined well-being.

Along the way we've learned that our communities are impacted by societal systems in different ways, and that these differences affect our mental health. Our guides approach important issues such as oppression and intergenerational trauma and invite you to join others in crafting solutions that help transform the health of our communities.

This guide will help you make your own Mad Map. Drawing from the input of hundreds of members of the Icarus Project community, it will take you step by step through the process of creating your own wellness documents. The guides help you identify and share what you need for support in times of crisis, with the safety of knowing that you are drawing inspiration from tried and true resources shared by people with lived experiences. We hope you will recognize your own experiences in what others have written--and thus discover language to describe your experiences and new tools to maintain your well-being and transform your community.

When you're finished we'd love to share your map with the Icarus community. By sharing our maps, we can identify our common struggles, inspire each other, teach each other how we can best be supported, and come together to transform the world around us. We envision a world where people create effective communities of support and for individual and collective liberation. Learn more about our network of local chapters, upcoming workshops and events, and how you can join the radical mental health movement at www.theicarus-project.net.

## How To Use This Guide

It's best to work through this guide from front to back. At each step we'll provide answers Icarus members gave to a set of questions you can use as inspiration for your own. Check all that apply. In the back you'll also find the same 15 questions and space to write your own.

Some people find reading about the experiences of others helps them better document their own, while others know what they want to say without any prompting. Either way, or somewhere in between, is OK. There is no right or wrong. In fact, you can even use this guide more than once as your life changes and you have new experiences. Similarly, writing our answers is just one way of mapping. Some people only use words in their maps, while others use art or diagrams. You might use the questions to start exploring and then find you'd like to map in a different way. We just want you to find whatever works best for you to tell your own story.

There are four sections in this guide. In Section I and II you'll find an introduction to oppression--what it is and how we experience it. Section III explores how we cope with it. Section IV asks how we can address oppression in our communities and achieve collective liberation. The Epilogue is where you'll find the questions and room to answer them to make your own map.

By the time you're finished you'll have a greater awareness of how oppression affects you and those around you. You'll also create your own Mad Map, which serves as a reminder document for yourself and the people around you about your wellness goals, warning signs, strategies for health, and who you trust to look out for your best interests when you're struggling.

Each section is designed for people at any stage of life--whether you're just starting to examine "madness" and oppression or you're looking for additional tools to identify needs and achieve your goals. We hope everybody will find inspiration and strategies that best suit their needs and those of their communities in this guide. Most importantly, we hope that we can all feel less alone and find hope in a harsh world through making our own maps.

Please note that reading about oppression and harm can sometimes be triggering in and of itself. Take care of yourself as you work your way through this text by making sure you're in a safe place where you can make adjustments for your safety and comfort as needed. Take breaks, breathe, sing, exercise, call a friend, take a nap, or engage in other kinds of care that nourishes you. Remember, you are worthy of love and you are part of a whole international community of people who are on this healing journey together.

Artist: Jacks McNamara

# Section I:
# Identifying Oppression

Artist: Mohammed Fayaz

## What is Oppression?

Oppression is the systemic and institutional abuse of power by one group at the expense of others and the use of force to maintain this dynamic. An oppressive system is built around the ideology of superiority of some groups and inferiority of others. This ideology makes those designated as inferior feel confined, 'less than,' and hinders the realization of their full spiritual, emotional, physical, and psychological well-being and potential. They are portrayed as "others" and are marginalized via social, mental, emotional, and physical violence which prevents their full inclusion in the community. All actions, systems, cultures, ideologies, and technologies which refuse to take full and equitable consideration of everyone and everything affected by them are aspects of oppression.

Oppression enables those in charge to have access to control resources and choices, while making those labeled as inferior vulnerable to poverty, violence, and early death. It is a set of processes, actions, and ideas that hinder the oppressed from exercising their full freedom of choice and having access to resources. These systems of inequity operate at internalized, institutional, and interpersonal levels to distribute advantages to some and to disadvantage others. Oppression is the tool that preserves existing unjust social relations and protects existing monopolies of power/privilege. It responds with violence when those with lesser power and privilege try to challenge these inequalities.

Oppression manifests itself as a systemic, structural, historically naturalized, and institutionalized violence that is normalized through hegemony, ideology, sheer repetition of dominant discourse, etc. It boxes the oppressed into categories of race, ethnicity, gender, class, and other divisions that supposedly distinguish the "normal" from the "abnormal." Those whose existence deviates from the norm are a threat to the dominant elites and oppression keeps them in line through shaming and enforcing their powerlessness.

Oppression actively provides unearned privileges and protections to some members of our community, allowing them to ignore the presence of classism, racism, ableism, fat hatred, sexism, homophobia, transphobia or any of the many systemic oppressive themes that live in our culture. It allows them to use this power and privilege, whether consciously or subconsciously, in order to achieve and acquire status or wealth at the expense of the oppressed. In a sense, this unearned privilege harms the oppressor as much as the oppressed because it keeps them sheltered and limits their ability to relate to a diverse range of people. The first step in transforming an oppressive system is to recognize our own privilege  and to understand the connection between our privilege and the suffering of others.

Patriarchy, mysogyny, sexism, heterosesxism, racism, ableism, ageism, militarism, colonialism are all  examples of oppression.

## What does oppression feel like?

☐ Oppression is closed doors. Whether it's me who closes a door because I can't cope, or whether somebody or something else closes it on me.

☐ Oppression is like when a great big bug steps on a little bug and squashes it. The big bug may claim to be important, beautiful, or even holy, but actually, it is just a large bug.

☐ When somebody pulls you inside a toilet and you use all your energy to just survive and, in the process, forget your aspirations and dreams

☐ It's like being in a river and always swimming against the current, but when I try to describe it to other people they often tell me that not only do they not feel it, they question whether it could be real. It's invisible and below the surface, but shapes our shorelines and our swimming bodies.

☐ Being pressed down or being distorted and crushed through the language and actions of others

☐ People climbing up and over you on a rope because they are stronger or better adapted to it than you are

☐ It's like being cornered, unable to escape. It's having little space for personal decision making and being forced against one's own sense of determination and will. It can be subtle, which is the most dangerous, especially when it morphs into self-oppression: the acceptance of the status quo forced upon oneself by others. Once such attitudes are internalized, one is trapped forever. One is unable to reach one's full potential due to outside factors; including socio-economics, trauma history, lack of social power, and institutionalization.

☐ Human-driven, soul-crushing forces that encourage negative self beliefs, dictate expression, strip away creativity, and control the use of time and tangible resources, often to the devastation of communities.

## How does oppression feel for you?

_____

_____

_____

_____

_____

_____

_____

_____

_____

_____

_____

_____

_____

# In what ways do you experience oppression?

Artist: Joey Wilbur

## *Racism:*

☐ A white-supremacist majority culture taught me that being non-white in appearance makes me less valuable than a white person

☐ I felt the pressure to be an "exception" to the 'rowdy Black girl'

☐ I was called racial slurs by people I knew and by strangers on the street

☐ I was insulted and slighted by people who assumed that I was stupid and ignorant because I am a woman of color

☐ Condescension by white authority figures who patronized me because of the history of my race

☐ Because of my race, I am assumed to be demure, diffident, and quietly passive as long as the white people allow our basic survival needs to be met

☐ As a mother of brown children, I experienced the difficulty of trying to find housing

- [ ] Authority figures talk down to me and I have to take it in order to get them to sign off on my case to move me along to the next person

- [ ] As a mixed race woman of color, I am expected to do a lot of care and emotional work for white folks, males especially

## Classism:

- [ ] I have been too poor to buy food

- [ ] I feel pressure to make our food stamps last the whole month

- [ ] I have slept outdoors because of being homeless, sometimes in cold weather

- [ ] I have not had enough opportunity for an education

- [ ] I work unfulfilling jobs to just barely get by

- [ ] I am forced to work minimum wage jobs because I can't get anything else

- [ ] I want to break out of all of this, but I can't access the tools to do it

- [ ] I lack adequate access to social services

- [ ] I can't access necessary medical care due to my low income

- [ ] I am considered inferior to others because of relative lack of wealth

- [ ] I feel shaming because I live below the poverty level

- [ ] Authority figures make assumptions about me because I am poor. A social worker leered at me and said, "If I don't like you, your benefits will disappear"

- [ ] I am told that my value is determined in comparison to the status quo and the external determination of value that others have of me

## Ableism:

- [ ] A sense of shame when having to visit social and government resource offices (i.e. "Yeah. You're 'disabled' by that. Hmmf")

- [ ] The inability of everyone else, including the Department of Mental Health, to see me/treat me/help me as a person

- [ ] I've been told numerous times that my episodes are why I'll never be in a successful relationship and why no one can love me

- [ ] I've been denied opportunities because they know my diagnosis and "the stress would be too much for [me] to handle"

- [ ] I was bullied because of my disability. I've had lots of comments made about me, even from strangers

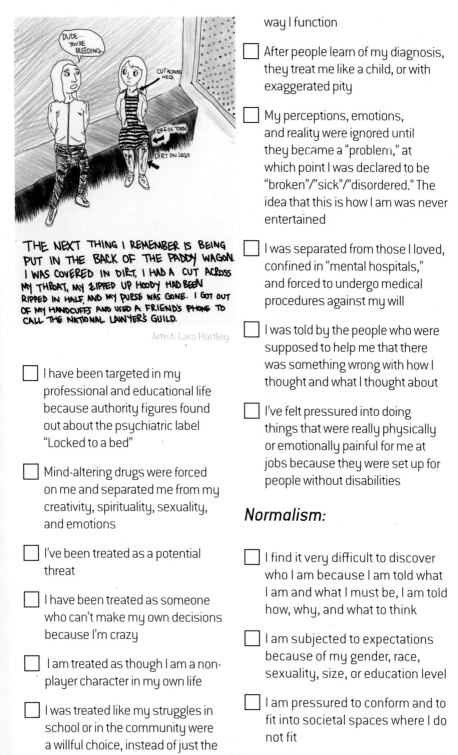

Artist: Cara Hartley

☐ I have been targeted in my professional and educational life because authority figures found out about the psychiatric label "Locked to a bed"

☐ Mind-altering drugs were forced on me and separated me from my creativity, spirituality, sexuality, and emotions

☐ I've been treated as a potential threat

☐ I have been treated as someone who can't make my own decisions because I'm crazy

☐ I am treated as though I am a non-player character in my own life

☐ I was treated like my struggles in school or in the community were a willful choice, instead of just the way I function

☐ After people learn of my diagnosis, they treat me like a child, or with exaggerated pity

☐ My perceptions, emotions, and reality were ignored until they became a "problem," at which point I was declared to be "broken"/"sick"/"disordered." The idea that this is how I am was never entertained

☐ I was separated from those I loved, confined in "mental hospitals," and forced to undergo medical procedures against my will

☐ I was told by the people who were supposed to help me that there was something wrong with how I thought and what I thought about

☐ I've felt pressured into doing things that were really physically or emotionally painful for me at jobs because they were set up for people without disabilities

## Normalism:

☐ I find it very difficult to discover who I am because I am told what I am and what I must be, I am told how, why, and what to think

☐ I am subjected to expectations because of my gender, race, sexuality, size, or education level

☐ I am pressured to conform and to fit into societal spaces where I do not fit

11

- [ ] I am fearful to share who I really am
- [ ] I have been rejected and sneered at
- [ ] I am unable to express my emotions without being slammed down or having the subject changed
- [ ] I feel inadequate as a result of my physical appearance, gender, or class

## Sexism:

- [ ] I have been given the message that the main uses I have in this world have to do with sex, cooking and cleaning
- [ ] As a rape survivor my fear is natural, yet it has so many times been decontextualized and seen as my problem, my mental illness
- [ ] I am constantly harassed on the street
- [ ] I was denied a leadership position because I am female
- [ ] I have experienced negative attitudes towards women
- [ ] I have been taunted and demeaned for being a woman
- [ ] I'm often treated like a sex object, talked down to, or ignored
- [ ] I have experienced domestic violence

- [ ] I have lived in an abusive situation that was made possible by patriarchal structures
- [ ] I was subjected to the controlling practices of an anxious partner
- [ ] Men deliberate my rights without giving me or other women any input
- [ ] I have experienced physical assault, hatred, and shame towards female genitalia
- [ ] The misogynist patriarchal and elitist society didn't allow me, as a poor child, to have the security and freedom to fully develop myself during my childhood and continues to put barriers around my security and freedom because I'm a woman
- [ ] I've been expected to sleep with many of my male coworkers because I was the only female at the workplace

## Heterosexism:

- [ ] I was denied healthcare because I'm trans
- [ ] I've had therapists and educators ask intrusive questions about my genitals because I'm trans
- [ ] I've been discriminated against at work because I was perceived as female
- [ ] I've been bullied for being queer

- [ ] I've had to stay away from places because their bathrooms weren't safe for me
- [ ] I have endured hurtful attitudes about my sexuality and gender
- [ ] I was given the "choice" between adhering to rigid rules and gender-normalizing religious practices or finding a way of coping on my own
- [ ] My genderqueer femme body and masculine attire freaked everyone out
- [ ] I was told I couldn't be gay. My hair was too long, my breasts were too big
- [ ] Being gay and having it be something that people avoid and pretend isn't there, instead of just treating it like it's part of human experience
- [ ] I feel that if I look too queer, I won't get a job
- [ ] If I stay out too late, I might get sexually assaulted
- [ ] I feel that even after you reach a certain level of academic or career success, the fear of losing everything you have never goes away
- [ ] Other queer people have told me that I'm queering incorrectly
- [ ] I was told that who I love is wrong

## Fundamentalism:

- [ ] I was force fed ideologies I didn't believe in
- [ ] I've been bullied for my religious beliefs
- [ ] I was brought up within a fundamentalist cult
- [ ] I have been asked to leave jobs because I would not agree to join a particular church
- [ ] Family members are too ashamed of my sexuality and gender
- [ ] Because of my gender and sexuality I have been left out of family events
- [ ] Religion has the power to set back women's rights and tell women what to do with their bodies
- [ ] I was damaged by being hammered daily with the idea that I am a sinner, a horrible person because of original sin, and only salvation keeps me from the fires of hell
- [ ] I was kept apart from "the world" by not being allowed to have school friends, not being allowed to wear socially acceptable clothes, watch tv, or listen to the radio

- [ ] I live in fear of anti-Semitism and deportation because of my background
- [ ] Patriarchal elements of the religion in which I was raised try to speak for me, even when what they want is outside US law, because they have an ownership attitude towards Jewish females
- [ ] I have lived in fear of arranged marriages

## Sizeism:

- [ ] I have been anorexic
- [ ] People give me opinions of my weight
- [ ] There is relentless fat-shaming in my family
- [ ] I'm small and skinny and have rude strangers demand to know if I have an "eating disorder"
- [ ] I have been told that I was 'too small' to do things like put up volleyball nets
- [ ] I've been laughed at in changing rooms
- [ ] People refused to help me find another size
- [ ] I've been pinched at a pub and asked about how "meaty" I am
- [ ] I get harassed for my weight most times when I leave the house

- [ ] I have been ignored when presenting my ideas or attempting to take over responsibilities because I'm big
- [ ] I have been looked over as an option for dates and sex
- [ ] I have had girlfriends (I'm cisfemale) be hesitant to include me when going out to meet men
- [ ] I have found it very difficult to find clothing that fit and was stylish and when I did it was majorly overpriced
- [ ] I have had my mother offer to pay for liposuction
- [ ] I have had someone I dated dump me for my size and then take me back after I agreed to lose weight
- [ ] My partner controlled what I ate and would plan dates around getting me exercise even if I didn't want that

## Ageism:

- [ ] I am often not taken seriously about an issue because of my age
- [ ] Because I was over 40, social services held open fewer possibilities for retraining for me in a going-back-to-work program
- [ ] Because of my age they withheld the possibility of funding study for an advanced degree

☐ I have been 'aged out' of the possibility of transitioning by certain professionals in the mental health communities

☐ My doctor is a conservative who believes that by my age I should be heterosexual and married

☐ Most children - gifted or not - are generally seen, understood, and treated as incapable of making meaningful contributions, feeling complex emotions, and processing complex information

☐ I have had my ideals dismissed because I was young

☐ As a bigger older ciswoman I am dismissed entirely as I leave the prime childbearing age and am not pleasing to look at

## What type of oppression have you experienced?

_____

_____

_____

_____

_____

_____

_____

_____

_____

_____

_____

_____

_____

_____

_____

_____

# What microaggressions do you experience?

- [ ] Members of my family ignore me almost anytime they see me

- [ ] People are impolite or ignore me because I am overweight

- [ ] Offensive compliments reaffirm stereotypes about my identity, such as when people think they're giving me some weird compliment when they say, "But you don't LOOK disabled"

- [ ] When someone ignores me or refuses to engage with me because I have an accent

- [ ] Casual use of psychiatric labels, such as calling the weather 'schizophrenic'

- [ ] When at meetings men talk to each other and don't even make eye contact with female co-workers

- [ ] Plus size clothes have their own section in stores instead of being with all the other sizes

- [ ] I took a call at work and the person said she had something important to say and did not want to talk to someone with an accent

- [ ] I hear jokes that replicate stereotypes about women

- [ ] Men impose their help without asking

- [ ] When people change their tone, speed, or attitude after finding out I have been in the psychiatric system or on disability

- [ ] I get this feeling all the time, that because I'm a young-looking adult woman, many men look down on me as immature

- [ ] Racially insensitive jokes

- [ ] Racially insensitive assumptions such as a friend saying to me "Well, can't you get some tribal land? And what about all that casino money?"

- [ ] When people give me instructions about how to articulate my opinions, such as when I have an opinion about something online and I get private messages telling me that, if I really wanted to make a point, I would say it in this way or in that way

- [ ] Racially charged comments about my appearance, such as when I'm buying coffee and the clerk tells me my daughter looks just like a little Eskimo

- [ ] When I'm standing in line with WIC groceries and the cashier tells me the food on the list is not the food I'm supposed to get and otherwise makes the checkout process half an hour longer than necessary

- [ ] I have been looked down on by co-workers at a waitressing job for being big and wearing tight pants, and one day when I did wear baggier pants one commented "oh, you look nice TODAY"

# What kind of microaggressions do you experience?

# Section II:
# Impact of Oppression

Artist: Mohammed Fayaz

Artist: JW Arndt

# How does oppression affect your feelings?

**Here are some emotions we identified:**

☐ Angry     ☐ Frustrated     ☐ Despondent

☐ Restless     ☐ Worthless     ☐ Disorientated

☐ Emotionally fatigued     ☐ Anxious     ☐ Defensive

☐ Enraged     ☐ Betrayed     ☐ Indignant

☐ Sad     ☐ Confused     ☐ Impatient

☐ Despaired     ☐ Isolated     ☐ Hostile

☐ Sorrowed     ☐ Physically Fatigued     ☐ Tense

☐ Helpless     ☐ Rebellious     ☐ Hurt

☐ Powerless     ☐ Empty     ☐ Disillusioned

☐ Ashamed     ☐ Humiliated     ☐ Alienated

☐ Worried     ☐ Distrustful

☐ Embarassed     ☐ Upset

# What other emotions do you feel when you experience oppression?

_____

_____

_____

_____

_____

_____

_____

# How does oppression affect your behavior?

**Here are some ways we described:**

- ☐ I hide.
- ☐ I overeat.
- ☐ I am unable to eat
- ☐ I oversleep
- ☐ I get insomnia
- ☐ I lash out
- ☐ I need physical distance from people
- ☐ I act crazy
- ☐ I become submissive
- ☐ I get violent
- ☐ I freeze
- ☐ I stop talking
- ☐ I stutter

- ☐ I collapse emotionally
- ☐ I stop taking care of myself
- ☐ I have nightmares
- ☐ I become passive aggressive
- ☐ I look for payback
- ☐ I become fearful of the future
- ☐ I feel my life is about to fall apart
- ☐ I disassociate
- ☐ I withdraw
- ☐ I retreat
- ☐ I escape into an imaginary world
- ☐ I convulse
- ☐ I freeze

# How does oppression affect the way you behave?

_____

_____

_____

_____

_____

_____

_____

_____

# How does oppresion make you sick?

**Here are some ways we identified:**

- [ ] I have tried to commit suicide
- [ ] I have suicidal thoughts
- [ ] I have panic attacks
- [ ] I get headaches
- [ ] I get stomach aches
- [ ] I experience depression
- [ ] I feel anxiety and paranoia
- [ ] I get persistent negative thoughts
- [ ] I feel dizziness
- [ ] I have developed eating disorders
- [ ] I abuse alcohol and/or drugs
- [ ] I have nightmares
- [ ] I experience sleep disturbance
- [ ] I have developed an ulcer

- [ ] All of my symptoms escalate
- [ ] Fear and paranoia of healthcare
- [ ] I self harm
- [ ] Self-hate
- [ ] I have insomnia
- [ ] It triggers manic episodes
- [ ] I experience PTSD
- [ ] I become "delusional"
- [ ] I become "psychotic"
- [ ] I dissociate
- [ ] I get rashes
- [ ] I develop compulsive behavior
- [ ] I exhibit obsessive behavior
- [ ] I get depressed

# How does oppression manifest in your body and mind?

_____

_____

_____

_____

_____

_____

_____

_____

# How do microaggressions compromise your wellness?

**Here is how some of us described the experience:**

- ☐ Self-shame
- ☐ Racing pulse
- ☐ I get really upset or agitated
- ☐ I exhibit excessive aggression
- ☐ I get violent
- ☐ I self-harm
- ☐ I get scared
- ☐ I get frustrated.
- ☐ I feel sad and memories come back in waves.
- ☐ I get distracted and lose focus
- ☐ I underperform
- ☐ I feel anxiety
- ☐ Intrusive thoughts

- ☐ Ear ringing
- ☐ Heat waves
- ☐ Flashbacks
- ☐ Agitation
- ☐ Fear
- ☐ Sadness
- ☐ Anxiety
- ☐ Hypervigilance
- ☐ Quickening of the pulse
- ☐ Anger
- ☐ Disorientation
- ☐ Dizziness
- ☐ Nausea
- ☐ Shakiness

# In what other ways do microaggressions compromise your wellness?

_____

_____

_____

_____

_____

_____

_____

_____

_____

# How does oppression affect the way you see yourself?

**Here are some ways we identified:**

- ☐ I feel really bad about myself
- ☐ I feel like I would rather just not be around
- ☐ I become egocentric
- ☐ I get angry with myself
- ☐ I have self-loathing
- ☐ I get caught in trying to fit an ideal of myself, rather than honestly being myself
- ☐ I question my ability to achieve goals
- ☐ I question if I will ever have happiness
- ☐ I am concerned that I am not "worthy" of being loved

- ☐ I feel so undermined
- ☐ I wonder if I'm just doing it all wrong, which quickly leads to feeling worse
- ☐ I feel distant from myself, fractured and uncertain about the future
- ☐ I feel unfocused and disengaged
- ☐ I blame myself
- ☐ I think, "Shouldn't have done that!"
- ☐ It makes it hard to feel strong and effective in the world
- ☐ Every time it happens, I have to restart the relationship with myself
- ☐ The shame and hate stay with me, it's very difficult to move past them

- [ ] The shame and hate stay with me, it's very difficult to move past
- [ ] I observe my mind whirling with anger, guilt, frustration
- [ ] I doubt myself
- [ ] I have decreased confidence in my ability to interact with others and to judge others
- [ ] I feel desperate and worthless going over old hurts

- [ ] I cannot cope with the idea of future hurts
- [ ] I have switching and 'shifts' that can look like mood swings from the outside, but aren't
- [ ] I often struggle with self hatred and shame
- [ ] I fee "less than" and inferior to my peers
- [ ] I often feel alienated from myself

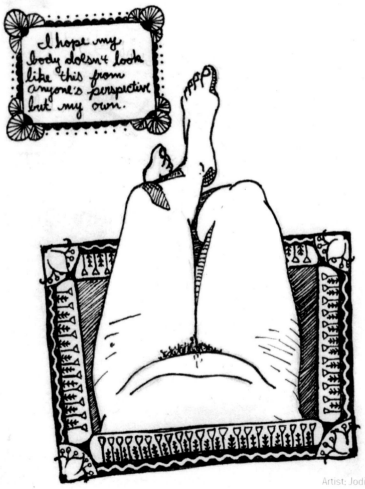

I hope my body doesn't look like this from anyone's perspective but my own.

Artist: Jodi Bentivegna

# How does oppression affect the way you perceive yourself?

_____

_____

_____

_____

_____

_____

_____

_____

# What are the social consequences of oppression?

**It affects our relationships with friends, family, and partners in these ways:**

- [ ] I have no friends
- [ ] My family doesn't talk to me
- [ ] I isolate myself
- [ ] I lash out in anger at my family and friends
- [ ] After I began to speak out, my family began treating me as a villain and telling me I am selfish
- [ ] Friends who don't understand oppression do not fully know me because they don't have that context
- [ ] I have to struggle with my internal conditioned reactions to sex that signal "danger, you're being used" so that I can experience it differently (meaning positively) or even experience it at all and not be checked out

- [ ] I feel resentful
- [ ] It makes me cautious
- [ ] I have difficulty trusting myself or others
- [ ] It makes communication very challenging
- [ ] It makes it difficult for me to be comfortable in group situations
- [ ] I have difficulty socializing with and expressing affection safely with others
- [ ] Sometimes act like I am being oppressed in relationships even when I am not

**It affects our broader community in these ways:**

☐ I isolate

☐ I'm alienated from all but my peers

☐ I still have a hard time believing I will be accepted and trusted by people

☐ My circles are somewhat small and I don't have relationships from when I was younger

☐ Sometimes I realize it takes me a long time to accomplish what other folks might see as simple communications

☐ I limit how much I connect with people around me in public places and in the community because of my lack of confidence and fear of not being accepted or respected

☐ Feeling that I cannot expect to feel safe in the broader world leads me to being timid and half present

☐ I don't feel a sense of belonging to my broader community

☐ My interactions are limited and superficial. I put on a happy face and stay in line

☐ I can't let anyone know my struggles

☐ I am utterly convinced that the wider community despises me and wants nothing to do with me

☐ I feel I have nothing to offer, or give, or do

☐ It makes it difficult to find a place and a way to contribute meaningfully to the community

**What other social consequences of oppression do you experience?**

_____

_____

_____

_____

_____

_____

_____

_____

_____

# How does oppression affect your ability to work?

**Here are some ways we identified:**

- [ ] I can't work when I am sleeping 24/7

- [ ] The medications make it harder for me to appear natural when interacting with coworkers or classmates

- [ ] I quit my jobs constantly, because there are behaviors that trigger my depressive periods and I can't do my job well

- [ ] I've had 42 jobs. It is damn near impossible for me to keep one. While highly skilled and resilient with a strong network, I can't keep myself in work for very long

- [ ] To be honest, I don't even know how I can really work...but of course I can't not, so it's just a perpetual painful mess

- [ ] Going to work is the hardest part

- [ ] Trying to interact with people who don't understand and don't want to makes me feel like giving up, so I keep to myself a lot and try my best to find jobs that don't require others

- [ ] I can't work anymore. I suspect that's a reaction to the oppression

- [ ] I have often debilitating anxiety related to PTSD, and it has kept me in very part time jobs, as I am worried to take on too much responsibility

- [ ] I am worried about having attacks and not feeling able to explain why I can't work

# How does oppression affect your daily life and your ability to work?

_____

_____

_____

_____

_____

_____

_____

_____

_____

## How does oppression affect your daily life?

**Here are some ways we identified:**

- [ ] It makes my life marginal, disorganized, and pathetic
- [ ] Fighting against overeating and other self-destructive habits has taken a lot of my time
- [ ] Mental illness is invisible
- [ ] Daily life hurts like hell
- [ ] Fifteen years of antipsychotics have taken their toll
- [ ] Constant pain
- [ ] Constantly containing my overflowing container
- [ ] Constant worry and feelings of being "lost"
- [ ] I wake up depressed...everyday is the same and there is nothing to do and no one to talk to

- [ ] I am always looking for police. I don't fear people in my neighborhood, I just fear police when I see them
- [ ] I put off things like cleaning or doing the dishes and lose myself online
- [ ] My daily life is a moment to moment challenge to experience my own perspective, be comfortable in my own skin, to find meaning and connection and a reason to continue living
- [ ] There are days when just having to get out of bed makes me want to cry
- [ ] Having to leave the house almost always breaks my heart
- [ ] Being responsible is difficult. It's hard to take care of myself

# Section III:
# Coping with Oppression

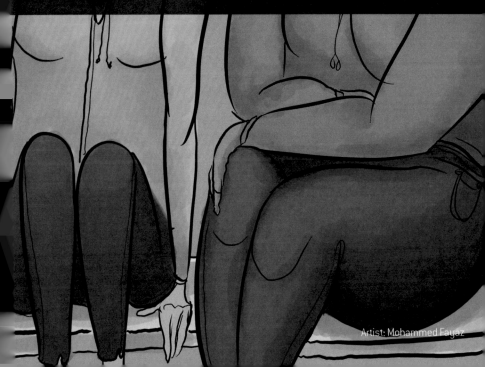

Artist: Mohammed Fayaz

Artist: Jacks McNamara

## How do you cope with the impact of oppression?

- [ ] Friends
- [ ] Exercise
- [ ] Eating healthy
- [ ] Yoga
- [ ] Creative expression
- [ ] Bicycling
- [ ] Stretching
- [ ] Fighting oppression!
- [ ] Activism!
- [ ] Meditation
- [ ] Laughter. Always laughter
- [ ] Social networking
- [ ] Sing

- [ ] Draw
- [ ] Martial arts
- [ ] Nature
- [ ] Icarus
- [ ] Writing
- [ ] Being part of a community
- [ ] Learn about it
- [ ] Pray for guidance
- [ ] Not giving up
- [ ] Knowing that I am not broken!
- [ ] Peer counseling
- [ ] Owning my opinions
- [ ] Humor

- [ ] Intellectualizing it
- [ ] Compassion
- [ ] Helping others
- [ ] Reading
- [ ] Playing with a pet
- [ ] Going to the gym
- [ ] Spiritual practice
- [ ] Therapy
- [ ] Homeopathics
- [ ] Bodywork
- [ ] Cuddling
- [ ] Routine
- [ ] Talking openly about it
- [ ] Sculpture
- [ ] Dance
- [ ] Film
- [ ] Photography
- [ ] Solidarity with others
- [ ] Art
- [ ] Music
- [ ] Picking my battles
- [ ] Trying to take care of myself
- [ ] Studying
- [ ] Thinking

- [ ] Breaking stereotypes
- [ ] Doing things that make me happy
- [ ] Speaking my mind
- [ ] Positive relationships
- [ ] Admitting when I'm not okay
- [ ] Taking a stand
- [ ] Educating myself
- [ ] Limiting exposure to oppressor
- [ ] Strengthening my personal love
- [ ] I developed talking points
- [ ] Advocacy
- [ ] Being open about my challenges
- [ ] Reading empowering statements, essays, and poems
- [ ] Organising
- [ ] Educating others
- [ ] Learning to say "no"
- [ ] Unafraid to tell the "truth" as I see it
- [ ] Power of Positive Thinking & Action
- [ ] Communicating to others
- [ ] Having a chosen family
- [ ] Contextualizing behavior within systemic violence so it is less shameful
- [ ] Seeing a counselor.
- [ ] Allowing ourselves to cry

- [ ] Reading about other people who experience oppression in order not to feel alone
- [ ] Going to rallies
- [ ] Writing
- [ ] Listening to cheerful music
- [ ] Reminding ourselves that not everyone will treat us poorly
- [ ] Reminding ourselves that the oppressors are at fault, not us
- [ ] Acknowledge the feeling, experiencing it in our bodies, and then, after a time, try to let it go
- [ ] Take deep breaths
- [ ] Turning feelings into action: finding a healthy venue for all the passion and emotional work that needs to be done
- [ ] Escapism into a book or a TV show is nice
- [ ] Meditate on simplicity and non-violent solutions
- [ ] Taking a stand
- [ ] Developing a good relationship with a trusted healthcare provider
- [ ] Allow ourselves to take a day or two to recover
- [ ] Remembering that life is not a race

- [ ] Reiki
- [ ] Detox
- [ ] Exercise
- [ ] Being in nature
- [ ] Caring for animals
- [ ] Nurturing people
- [ ] Being a friend and teacher for others
- [ ] Writing and reading
- [ ] Art
- [ ] Expressing the inexpressible
- [ ] Venting
- [ ] Reminding ourselves that we love life
- [ ] Spiritual practices
- [ ] Doing more rather than just existing
- [ ] Engage in self care
- [ ] Reaching out for support
- [ ] Deep breaths
- [ ] Self-talk
- [ ] Exercise
- [ ] Sleep

Artist: Eddy Falconer

## How else can you cope with the impact of oppression?

_____

_____

_____

_____

_____

_____

_____

_____

_____

_____

_____

_____

_____

_____

_____

_____

# How do you navigate triggering situations?

Artist: Jess Rankine

☐ Try to stay cool

☐ Detach as quickly as possible

☐ Listen to peaceful music

☐ Paint

☐ Advise the person who triggered the sensation that you need to take a moment and, say, get a glass of water

☐ Reach out to others if you feel too overwhelmed

☐ Let people know how they are affecting you

☐ Disengage or go for a walk

☐ Recognize where the anxiety is coming from

☐ Stay in your comfort zone with the people you know until you find someone trusted you can confide in

## What helps you navigate triggering situations? How can others help you?

_____

_____

_____

_____

_____

_____

_____

_____

_____

_____

_____

_____

_____

_____

_____

_____

_____

_____

_____

## How can people help you?
## How can we help each other?

- [ ] Don't tell me to "Snap out of it" or "It will be alright"
- [ ] Don't ignore me
- [ ] Normalize my feelings
- [ ] Validate me
- [ ] Name the oppression
- [ ] Make connections with others who have similar experiences
- [ ] Listen to me
- [ ] Don't try to fix me
- [ ] Be present
- [ ] Hear and acknowledge the experience
- [ ] Distract me
- [ ] Tell me a joke or share funny stories
- [ ] Watch a movie with me
- [ ] Talk to me about superficial topics, like celebrities or popular culture
- [ ] Help me focus on the things I like
- [ ] Appreciate my voice
- [ ] Don't tell me how I feel
- [ ] Speak about positive things
- [ ] Invite me to get together
- [ ] Come visit
- [ ] Bring over a treat

- [ ] Make me some tea
- [ ] Bring me flowers
- [ ] Show me you love me
- [ ] Join in on the action
- [ ] Believe
- [ ] Validate my experience
- [ ] Normalize
- [ ] Say it is not okay
- [ ] Help me up to a better plane of existence
- [ ] Run me a bath
- [ ] Getting me comfy clothes to change into
- [ ] Don't discourage my dreams
- [ ] Believe I am capable of anything despite my struggles and obstacles
- [ ] Educate yourself
- [ ] Acknowledge that you are capable of racist acts without being racist
- [ ] Be an ear, even if you don't agree with me
- [ ] Engage in intellectual debate
- [ ] Don't shoot down my ideas
- [ ] Treat me like an adult

- [ ] Tell me that you love me regardless of what happens to me
- [ ] Stay with me
- [ ] Give me space
- [ ] Be aware
- [ ] Have patience
- [ ] Be understanding
- [ ] Show compassion
- [ ] Remind me of my skills
- [ ] Help me use some my skills
- [ ] Be there for me
- [ ] Don't abandon me
- [ ] Help me by reducing pressure
- [ ] Remembering that it takes me time to heal
- [ ] Don't pressure me
- [ ] Accept my feelings
- [ ] Don't give unsolicited advice
- [ ] Remind me of things that have helped me in the past
- [ ] Don't say, "I know exactly how you feel"
- [ ] Hug me
- [ ] Believe in what I say
- [ ] Hold my hand
- [ ] Offer to call my therapist for me
- [ ] Offer to run errands

**In what other ways can people help you? What is helpful? What isn't?**

_____

_____

_____

_____

_____

_____

_____

_____

_____

_____

# Section IV:
# Transforming our Communities

Artist: Mohammed Fayaz

## Where can we begin to address oppression in our communities?

We can begin by talking about it. There are many benefits to talking about oppression in our communities. These include:

☐ When you understand and acknowledge what is really happening and why, you can address it directly and begin to actually problem-solve effectively. There are no benefits - only costs - to inequality.

☐ We need to look at all the ways people are hurt by oppression because that could lead to people telling the truth about how oppressive our society is, and that could hopefully lead to positive changes.

☐ People would know that they're not alone.

☐ If we don't explore it, we leave it up to the authorities, and their perspectives are important but limited. If we do explore it, we do have a chance to reduce the amount of madness and oppression and to improve personally and communally.

☐ Oppression must be understood in order to counter it. In a community setting, the community as a whole must understand how oppression is generated by groups and directed against individual members of the community.

☐ Talking about these issues in a safe way can only have a positive effect on everyone.

☐ It can help us bond: we can learn greater depth in how to support people who are challenged by emotions or behaviors that interfere with their life

☐ More compassion could be accessed through exploring oppression. People tend to dehumanize what they do not understand.

☐ The community will benefit because they will become more aware of their suffering and may reach out from the shadows to join programs or start new ones so oppression will become a nonword.

☐ Exposing oppression helps the individual get a sense of justice and it helps the community to see the oppression and stop it.

## How can you begin to address oppression in your community?

_____

_____

_____

_____

_____

_____

_____

_____

_____

_____

_____

_____

_____

_____

_____

_____

_____

## Steps we can take to mitigate oppression include:

- ☐ Do the work. Educate yourself. People need to educate themselves, speak up, be okay with feeling uncomfortable

- ☐ Join social causes. Contribute work in your own way, whether marching in the streets or stuffing envelopes

- ☐ Sign petitions

- ☐ Speak at City Council meetings

- ☐ Educate your children

- ☐ End the silence. Talk about it. Name it. Show support

- ☐ Raise awareness: talk to friends

- ☐ Be outspoken

- ☐ Confront 'isms' as they arise

- ☐ Be a good ally

- ☐ Help show your community that we are here

- ☐ Teach children that homeless people have feelings and that LGBT parents are just like theirs

- ☐ People could educate themselves about PTSD and understand that it's a part of who I am, and they'll appreciate me, and other sufferers, all the more for it

- ☐ Prevent bullying

- ☐ Take actions together and plan actions in groups. They could educate themselves on oppression, privilege, racism, cultural competency, and so forth

- [ ] Support families in your communities. Make establishments intergenerational to include children and the elderly

- [ ] Demand that the homeless be allowed to sleep in their homeless camps.They could build a support system for activists and those fighting oppression and encourage their efforts and their voice and their struggle

- [ ] I believe the first step is to cultivate an open mind, to believe that we are all capable of healing and change

- [ ] Participate in letter-writing campaigns to companies and complain

- [ ] Accept that there are people like me and that I desire to help them

- [ ] Accept that I am able to do art and poetry because of my life's journey

- [ ] Go to rallies and marches to support others

- [ ] Sign petitions and email politicians

- [ ] Display anti-racist stickers

- [ ] Talk to others to raise awareness

- [ ] Create an inner peace and that is indestructible

## Steps we have taken to mitigate oppression include:

- [ ] I now have a yearning to change the situations and bring others into the light of understanding, that life is beautiful and precious

- [ ] I believe the feelings of oppression have given me immense compassion and understanding

- [ ] I have written and directed short plays, and drawn and painted lovely pictures. I could not have done those things had I not been in such pain

- [ ] It's made me stronger in my faith

- [ ] I've made friends and deepened relationships

- [ ] I've done spoken word

- [ ] I've made zines

- [ ] I helped start or participated in several anti-oppression movements

- [ ] Sometimes I think about how many people may feel similar to the way I feel, and it inspires me to write zines or fiction, thinking there may be this unknown-to-me audience that might take value in my words

- [ ] I found acceptance in a community that values people for who they are

- [ ] I found a sense of liberation in beginning to accept myself completely

- [ ] I'm trying to engage other users/ survivors in creating a community that focuses on alternative conceptualizations of mental health and well-being and on political action to bring about systemic change

☐ The only "cure" for powerlessness is social and political activism - my only concern is about caring for the ones who get burnt out and cannot find a caring community, and that is something we need to work on as a community

☐ I have learned how to strengthen my chakras and my aura so as not to be bombarded with other peoples negative energy

☐ I prioritize my own health, safety, and self-expression

☐ I try to be good to others, to be the best person I can be to make the world more tolerable

☐ I feel a strong need to change it all, or at least stir it up with a big spoon

☐ I tend to philosophise at length in the comfort of the bedroom, take walks outside, and write poetry to do justice to such sentiments and not get totally burnt out

☐ I organize to build power with our people to overcome our oppressions

## What other ideas do you have for transforming your community?

_____

_____

_____

_____

_____

_____

_____

_____

_____

_____

_____

_____

_____

_____

# Epilogue:
# Creating your own Mad Map

Artist: Jacks McNamara

As you made your way through this book did you check off any items or answer the questions? Below you'll find all the questions repeated--you might want to write your answers here, including any of the items you checked, so you have them organized in one place. Afterward, think about how you would like to represent your answers: lists, drawings, a vision board, a wall dedicated to mapping, photo maps, a journal, or an essay all are ways community members have used to showcase their map. You can choose the one that best suits your style, or even mix and match.

Once you know how you want to build your map, choose a setting that is right for you. Some people like to answer these questions in private, with a friend, in a group, or with support from our online community. The Icarus Project also offers mad mapping workshops so you can make your map with the help of a skilled facilitator.

We suggest you take it easy, be honest with yourself, honor your feelings, and reach out for support so you can safely recover from any triggers sharing this information may cause.

If you end up adding your own questions, want to anonymously share your map with others, or want to use this guide for a group we'd love your additions to this community project! Email madmaps@theicarusproject.net to let us know.


- What does oppression feel like?
- In what ways do you experience oppression?
- Do you experience daily microaggressions?
- Does oppression affect how you feel?
- Does oppression affect how you behave?
- How does oppression impact your mental, emotional and physical health?
- How does your body react to microaggressions?
- How does oppression affect the way you perceive yourself?
- What are some social consequences of oppression that you experience?
- How do you cope with the impact of oppression?
- How do you navigate triggering situations?
- How can people help you? How can we help each other?
- Where can we begin to address oppression in our communities?
- What steps can your community take to mitigate oppression? What steps can your community take to mitigate oppression?

_____

_____

_____

_____

_____

_____

_____

_____

_____

_____

_____

_____